THE BOOK OF
2Kings

ONE CHAPTER A DAY

GoodMorningGirls.org

The Book of 2 Kings

Welcome to Good Morning Girls! We are so glad you are joining us.

God created us to walk with Him, to know Him, and to be loved by Him. He is our living well, and when we drink from the water He continually provides, His living water will change the entire course of our lives.

> *Jesus said: "Whoever drinks of the water that I will give him will never be thirsty again. The water that I will give him will become in him a spring of water welling up to eternal life." ~ John 4:14 (ESV)*

So let's begin.

The method we use here at GMG is called the **SOAK** method.

- ❏ **S**—The S stands for *Scripture*—Read the chapter for the day. Then choose 1-2 verses and write them out word for word. (There is no right or wrong choice—just let the Holy Spirit guide you.)

- ❏ **O**—The O stands for *Observation*—Look at the verse or verses you wrote out. Write 1 or 2 observations. What stands out to you? What do you learn about the character of God from these verses? Is there a promise, command or teaching?

- ❏ **A**—The A stands for *Application*—Personalize the verses. What is God saying to you? How can you apply them to your life? Are there any changes you need to make or an action to take?

- ❏ **K**—The K stands for *Kneeling in Prayer*—Pause, kneel and pray. Confess any sin God has revealed to you today. Praise God for His word. Pray the passage over your own life or someone you love. Ask God to help you live out your applications.

SOAK God's word into your heart and squeeze every bit of nourishment you can out of each day's scripture reading. Soon you will find your life transformed by the renewing of your mind!

Walk with the King!

Courtney

WomenLivingWell.org, GoodMorningGirls.org

Join the GMG Community

Share your daily SOAK on *Facebook.com/GoodMorningGirlsWLW*

Instagram: WomenLivingWell #GoodMorningGirls

GMG Bible Coloring Chart

COLORS	KEYWORDS
PURPLE	God, Jesus, Holy Spirit, Saviour, Messiah
PINK	women of the Bible, family, marriage, parenting, friendship, relationships
RED	love, kindness, mercy, compassion, peace, grace
GREEN	faith, obedience, growth, fruit, salvation, fellowship, repentance
YELLOW	worship, prayer, praise, doctrine, angels, miracles,power of God, blessings
BLUE	wisdom, teaching, instruction, commands
ORANGE	prophecy, history, times, places, kings, genealogies, people, numbers, covenants, vows, visions, oaths, future
BROWN/GRAY	Satan, sin, death, hell, evil, idols, false teachers, hypocrisy, temptation

Introduction to the Book of 2 Kings

In 2 Kings, we saw David and Solomon in all their royal splendor. But Solomon sinned and the kingdom was divided. So, in 2 Kings we will sadly see, one bad king after another fall. We will also see the spiritual decline and eventual captivity of both kingdoms.

While none of the kings of Israel did what was right in the eyes of the Lord, four of the kings of Judah did. Joash, Uzziah, Hezekiah and Josiah attempted to remove the idolatry from Judah, but in the end, it was not enough.

The ministry and miracles of the prophet Elisha are a bright light in these dark times. Elijah performed 7 miracles in 2 Kings, but a double portion of the spirit was given to Elisha. So, in 2 Kings, it is recorded that he performed 14 miracles.

God continually raised up prophets to speak to the nation of Israel and to tell them to turn from their wicked ways, but they did not listen. As a result, **2 Kings 10:32 says, "In those days the Lord began to cut off a part of Israel."**

Although God was powerfully at work in the lives of these prophets, Israel still would not turn from their idols and follow God wholeheartedly. As a result, Israel was taken into captivity by Assyria in 721BC and Judah was taken into captivity by Babylon in 586BC.

At the end of 2 Kings, the Babylonian empire destroys the temple and the people are taken into exile. But we are given a glimmer of hope in the end, because God is not done with his people.

We can learn more about these kings by reading 1 & 2 Chronicles and studying the prophets that prophesied during this time period. Those prophets include Amos and Hosea, who were sent to Israel and Obadiah, Joel, Isaiah, Micah, Nahum, Habakkuk, Zephaniah and Jeremiah, who were sent to Judah.

The Purpose: 2 Kings gives the history of the kings and prophets of Israel and Judah, leading up to their exile.

The Author: Although the author is anonymous, tradition holds that 2 Kings was written by Jeremiah.

Time Period: This book was written around 550 B.C.

Key Verse: 2 Kings 10:32: *"In those days the Lord began to cut off a part of Israel."*

The Outline:

The Ministries of Elijah and Elisha (1:1-8:15)

1. Ahaziah reigns (1)
2. Elijah is taken to heaven and Elisha succeeds Elijah (2)

3. Elisha and the war against Moab (3)

4. Elisha's ministry to the widow, Shunammite & prophets (4)

5. Elisha heals Naaman (5)

6. Elisha, the recovered ax head and the chariots of fire (6)

7. Elisha's promise of food (7)

The Kings of Israel and Judah until the Exile of Israel (8:16-17:41)

1. Jehoram &Ahaziah of Judah (8:16-24)

2. Jehu of Israel (9 & 10)

3. Athaliah and Joash of Judah (11 & 12)

4. Jehoahaz and Jehoash of Israel (13)

5. Amaziah of Judah & Jeroboam II of Israel (14)

6. Azariah of Judah, Zechariah of Israel, Shallum of Israel, Menahem of Israel, Pekahiah of Israel, Pekah of Israel, & Jotham of Judah (15)

7. Ahaz of Judah (16)

8. Hoshea of Israel & the exile of Israel (17)

Judah from Hezekiah to Babylonian Exile (18-24)

1. Hezekiah (18-20)

2. Manasseh & Amon (21)

3. Josiah, Jehoahaz, & Jehoiakim (22-23)

4. Jehoiachin & Zedekiah (24)

The fall and captivity of Judah (25)

Despite God giving Israel multiple chances to repent and turn from their wicked ways, they continued in their sin and idolatry. As a result, God's judgement was upon them. But even through all of the dark times, God was still at work among His people. Eventually, a redeemer would come from the royal line of David because God keeps his promises to his people. We serve a faithful God, who loves us.

So let's get started studying His word! Some of the chapters are quite long, so be sure to leave at least 20 minutes for your reading each day. I can't wait to see how God reveals himself personally to each of us, as we read the book of 2 Kings together, chapter by chapter.

Keep walking with the King!

Courtney

Do not be afraid.

2 Kings 1:15

Reflection Question:

After King Ahab died, his son Ahaziah took the throne but soon after, he had a serious accident. Ahaziah sent messengers to the god, Baal-zebub, to find out if he would recover. Instead, he received word that Elijah said he would die. Ahaziah did not like this answer and so he sent a captain and fifty men to question Elijah, but fire from heaven came down and consumed them. After repeating this mistake twice, finally his captain came with humility. Elijah went with him to meet Ahaziah and once again predicted that he would die. Then Ahaziah died, fulfilling Elijah's prophecy.

In his times of trouble, Ahaziah turned to the wrong god. Since his god was not real, he got no real help. We must be careful where we look for answers. We must not avoid God just because we are afraid that we may not like his answers. Who or where do you turn in times of trouble? Are the people that you turn to godly and wise? Is God the first place you turn or last?

2 Kings 1

S—The S stands for ***Scripture***

O—The O stands for ***Observation***

A—The A stands for ***Application***

K—The K stands for ***Kneeling in Prayer***

And Elisha said,

"Please let there be a double portion

of your spirit on me."

2 Kings 2:9

Reflection Question:

As the prophet Elijah is about to be taken up into heaven, he offers Elisha anything he asks. Elisha asks for a double portion of his spirit. Then chariots of fire appear, and Elijah is taken up in a whirlwind. After this, Elisha takes Elijah's cloak and strikes the water and parts the Jordan, demonstrating that he had indeed received the double portion he asked for.

In a tender moment, Elisha had the opportunity to ask for anything he desired. He chose to ask for more of God's power. If you had the same choice, what would you choose? Also, we see the two men cross the Jordan together in verse 8. Then Elisha crosses alone in verse 14. It is not easy to step out alone and simply trust in God as Elisha did. Is there an area in your life where God is calling you to step out and walk alone? How can you trust God more as you walk this path alone?

S—The S stands for *Scripture*

O—The O stands for *Observation*

A—The A stands for *Application*

K—The K stands for *Kneeling in Prayer*

The word of the Lord

is with him.

2 Kings 3:12

Reflection Question:

The king of Israel joined with 2 other kings against Moab and yet he still was not finding victory. They were without water and so they called for Elisha. Elisha called for a musician and notice how God used the musician to usher in God's word to the prophet. (If you serve in music ministry, be encouraged—you have a sacred ministry!) The Lord responded in mercy and not only sent a flash flood to help them survive, but he also gave them the victory,

Once the kings were not only losing but also their people were about to die of thirst, they realized this was a spiritual issue and they needed God. Elisha told them, the water they were asking for was "a light thing in the sight of the Lord" and that God would give them even more—victory!

Sometimes we are just like these three kings and we wait too long to seek the Lord's help. We do not realize that some of our physical issues are spiritual issues. Things that we think are simply too hard for even God, we fail to pray for. Are you fighting a battle right now that you feel defeated in? Write a prayer below asking God to deliver you. Our God is able!

2 Kings 3

S—The S stands for *Scripture*

O—The O stands for *Observation*

A—The A stands for *Application*

K—The K stands for *Kneeling in Prayer*

Elisha said to her, "Go outside,

borrow vessels from all your neighbors

Then go in and shut the door behind yourself

and pour into all these vessels."

2 Kings 4:3, 4

Reflection Question:

Elisha performed many miracles, but we see that it required radical faith from the widow, the Shunammite woman, the person who took the next bite of the stew, and the servant who fed the men. Elisha did not miraculously make the oil appear for the widow. She had to go to her neighbors and tell them about her situation. She had to ask to borrow their vessels and she only received as much oil as she was willing to ask from her neighbors. She had to die to herself and her pride and ask for help, in order to see the power of God displayed in her life. But it was in private, when the door was shut, that the oil flowed.

Is there an area in your life where you need help? Is it hard for you to let others know when you have a need? Write the need below and consider who you could ask to help meet this need. Perhaps you need to go to your pastor, a friend or a neighbor. Trust that letting others know your need, could be the very way in which the Lord wants to provide for you.

S—The S stands for **Scripture**

O—The O stands for **Observation**

A—The A stands for **Application**

K—The K stands for **Kneeling in Prayer**

Behold, I know that there is no God

in all the earth but in Israel.

2 Kings 5:15

Reflection Question:

Naaman, a mighty man of valor, was at the top of his game but he was dying of leprosy. A brave little girl from Israel told him about the prophet Elisha. If she had been wrong, she would have been in danger, but she was right. Elisha sent word that Naaman should wash in the Jordan seven times to be healed but this did not meet Naaman's expectations. It angered him. He expected Elisha to come to him and cure him. Instead, it required Naaman to act in faith and do it himself. Naaman was healed without Elisha being nearby and as a result, God received all the glory.

Elisha repeatedly asked those who were seeking the Lord's help to take part in their miracles. It required faith from those who sought the Lord. As a result, God received all the praise, rather than Elisha. Elisha's instructions were simple yet very difficult for a prideful man. Naaman had to overcome his pride in order to receive from the Lord. Reflect on your own life. In what area do you struggle with pride especially when it comes to following the Lord? And in what area are you leaning too hard on another person, rather than on God?

S—The S stands for *Scripture*

O—The O stands for *Observation*

A—The A stands for *Application*

K—The K stands for *Kneeling in Prayer*

Do not be afraid,

for those who are with us

are more than those

who are with them.

2 Kings 6:16

Reflection Question:

Elisha reassured his servant that he had nothing to fear because they had spiritual protection that he could not see. Elisha prayed and ask the Lord to open the servant's eyes. When his eyes were opened, he saw the mountain full of horses and chariots of fire, all around them. God struck the Syrians with blindness and Elisha and his servant were safe.

Elisha did not try to explain to the servant the reality of God's protection for them, instead he prayed and asked the Lord to open his eyes. God answered Elisha's prayer. The servant had to see it for himself to believe it. There is a spiritual reality around us that we cannot see, but it is real. God is with us. Is there someone you love who is blind to the spiritual realities of God? Though God may want to use you to point that person toward the truth, only God can open their eyes. Write a prayer below and ask the Lord to open their eyes.

S—The S stands for *Scripture*

O—The O stands for *Observation*

A—The A stands for *Application*

K—The K stands for *Kneeling in Prayer*

But Elisha said,

"Hear the word of the Lord."

2 Kings 7:1

Reflection Question:

The word of the Lord came to Elisha and he prophesied that the prices of food would drop within 24 hours. The king's captain doubted Elisha and even joked that perhaps God would just drop food from heaven. As a result, a judgement was placed on the captain that he would see the prophecy fulfilled, but not get to share in the blessing. Then God fought for Israel by simply causing the Syrians to hear the sound of chariots, horses and a great army. When they fled, they left all their food in the camp behind. And then it happened according to the word of the Lord, the prices of food went down and the captain saw but was trampled by the people.

May we never doubt the word of God or the power of God to work in ways beyond our imagination or understanding. Unbelief will cause us to miss out on the blessings of the Lord! In what area of your life are struggling with unbelief? Pray and ask the Lord to sustain, strengthen and deepen your faith.

S—The S stands for *Scripture*

O—The O stands for *Observation*

A—The A stands for *Application*

K—The K stands for *Kneeling in Prayer*

So, the woman arose
and did according to the word
of the man of God.

2 Kings 8:2

Reflection Question:

Once again, the Shunammite woman and her son were saved by God, through Elisha. Elisha warns her of a famine in the land and so she arises and does exactly as he tells her to do. For seven years, they sojourn in the land of the Philistines. Upon her return, God intervenes in the timing of her appearance before the king, and all of her land is restored to her.

If you turn back to 2 Kings 4:8-10, you will remember that the way that the Shunammite woman connected with the prophet Elisha was by urging him to eat some of her food. So, whenever he passed by, he would stop and eat at her house. From there, she asked her husband to make a room for him with a bed, chair and lamp. God used this woman's hospitality and her 'bed and breakfast' to meet his needs.

God saw the Shunammite woman's generosity toward the man of God and blessed her. Have you ever helped care for the need of a pastor, a Sunday School teacher, or a missionary? Is there someone right now in ministry, who has a need you could meet? Write it below and ask the Lord to give you the ability to help meet that need.

S—The S stands for *Scripture*

O—The O stands for *Observation*

A—The A stands for *Application*

K—The K stands for *Kneeling in Prayer*

"What peace can there be,
so long as the whorings
and the sorceries of your mother
Jezebel are so many?"

2 Kings 9:22

Reflection Question:

As the queen to king Ahab, Jezebel plotted evil against the prophets of God. She called herself a prophet and led the people of Israel astray into idolatry and immorality. When Jehu was anointed king, it was foretold that he would be used to avenge on Jezebel the blood of the prophets. And so, it came to pass, Jezebel was not only killed but she was trampled by horses and eaten by dogs.

God was greatly angered at Jezebel and her wickedness. Her influence is spoken of in Revelation 2:20: *"But I have this against you, that you tolerate that woman Jezebel, who calls herself a prophetess and is teaching and seducing my servants to practice sexual immorality and to eat food sacrificed to idols."* The problem in the church in Revelation was not that the evil existed, but that the church tolerated it. We must be aware that there are false teachers, both women and men, in the church today. Where do you see false teaching creeping into the church today? How can you grow in wisdom and remain faithful to God's Word, so that you will not be led astray?

S—The S stands for *Scripture*

O—The O stands for *Observation*

A—The A stands for *Application*

K—The K stands for *Kneeling in Prayer*

Come with me,

and see my zeal for the Lord.

2 Kings 10:16

Reflection Question:

Jehu carried out what was right in the eyes of the Lord by wiping out the house of Ahab and destroying the house of Baal, along with Baal's prophets. Jehu was zealous for God and he showed it, by wiping out evil in the land.

Zeal is passion and Jehu's passion caused him to obey the Lord even though it was not safe or comfortable to do. Although Jehu in the end, was far from perfect, God still blessed his zeal. God wants us to be passionate about doing what is right. Are you passionate for the things of God? What is something that requires courage or going outside your comfort zone, that God is asking you to do? Is there something you need to get rid of your life that is displeasing to him?

S—The S stands for *Scripture*

O—The O stands for *Observation*

A—The A stands for *Application*

K—The K stands for *Kneeling in Prayer*

And Jehoiada made a covenant

between the Lord and the king and people,

that they should be the Lord's people.

2 Kings 11:17

Reflection Question:

Jehosheba was brave when she hid Joash in the temple. For six dark years, the boy hid there, and he was safe because Athaliah did not spend time in the temple of the Lord. When Joash became king, the priest made a covenant between the Lord, the king and the people. It was a time of renewal in the land, as all the people recommitted themselves to obey and serve God.

Sometimes the Lord asks us to give things up for him, but other times he just wants us to live committed to him. Sometimes we neglect our time with him or stop doing something good because we are too busy or distracted. Is there an area of your life that you need to recommit to the Lord? Write a prayer of recommitment below.

S—The S stands for *Scripture*

O—The O stands for *Observation*

A—The A stands for *Application*

K—The K stands for *Kneeling in Prayer*

And Jehoash did what was right
in the eyes of the Lord all his days,
because Jehoiada the priest instructed him.

2 Kings 12:2

Reflection Question:

Jehoash did what was right in the eyes of the Lord, as long as the priest Jehoida instructed him. After the priest's death, 2 Chronicles 24:15-22 tells us that Jehoash listened to the wrong advisers and was led astray. As a result, he died a tragic death.

Jehoash had grown used to the strong influence and guidance of the priest in his life. Once he was gone, he did not seem to know how to handle difficult decisions on his own. Who do you turn to for advice and guidance? If that person was not in your life, would you have the wisdom to make good decisions on your own? Is there anyone that you listen to that gives you bad advice? Who should you stop listening to?

S—The S stands for **Scripture**

O—The O stands for **Observation**

A—The A stands for **Application**

K—The K stands for **Kneeling in Prayer**

But the Lord was gracious to them

and had compassion on them.

2 Kings 13:23

Reflection Question:

Elisha commanded Jehoash to the strike the ground with his arrows. The number of times the arrows hit the ground, would be his number of victories. Jehoash half-heartedly shot three arrows into the ground and then stopped. This angered Elisha because he knew this was limiting the number of victories that God would give them.

It's interesting to see the mixture of God's sovereignty and man's responsibility in this story. God wanted to give them victory, but they did not receive the full victory they could have had, because of Jehoash's lack of fervor. He should have taken all of his arrows and shot them all into the ground, fully pursuing the victory. His heart and passion were not into it, but God was still gracious and compassionate to his people. He did give them three victories. Is there an area in your life where you need victory? Are you passionately pursuing it or sitting back waiting on God to deliver it to you? Are you battling a sin? God wants to give us victory, but he also wants us to be willing to do whatever it takes to have full victory.

S—The S stands for **Scripture**

O—The O stands for **Observation**

A—The A stands for **Application**

K—The K stands for **Kneeling in Prayer**

Why should you provoke trouble

so that you fall?

2 Kings 14:10

Reflection Question:

Amaziah was proud of his success in battle, so he challenged Jehoash to meet him face to face in battle. Jehoash warned him that his pride of his win was going to provoke trouble and cause him to fall. But Amaziah would not listen and in the end, he faced defeat.

Amaziah's pride cause him to start a battle that should have never been started. He was encouraged by his own enemy to not provoke him and yet he refused to listen to the warning. Has your pride ever caused you to get into a fight with someone? Do you listen when you are warned, or do you let your emotions get the best of you? If there is someone you are in a fight with right now, consider, how you can be a peacemaker in the situation?

S—The S stands for **Scripture**

O—The O stands for **Observation**

A—The A stands for **Application**

K—The K stands for **Kneeling in Prayer**

And he did what was right

in the eyes of the Lord.

2 Kings 15:3

Reflection Question:

In this chapter, we see the rise and fall of multiple kings. Some reign for a short time and change rapidly, while others are very long. We see a contrast of both the good and evil kings but sadly, we see a repeat of idolatry in Israel that does not seem to be dealt with.

After each of the kings are named, along with their age and years of their reign, it says that they either did what was right in the eyes of the Lord or what was evil in the sight of the Lord. If a story was being written about your life, would the author say these words about you, "she did what was right in the eyes of the Lord." Why or why not?

2 Kings 15

S—The S stands for **Scripture**

O—The O stands for **Observation**

A—The A stands for **Application**

K—The K stands for **Kneeling in Prayer**

He did not do what was right

in the eyes of the Lord his God.

2 Kings 16:2

Reflection Question:

Ahaz had a good father named Jotham and was in the lineage of David, but he did not follow in their footsteps. Instead he rejected his godly heritage and did not do what was right in the eyes of the Lord. It's interesting to note that Judah had a mix of good and bad kings while Israel had just one type—ungodly kings. Sadly, Ahaz followed after Israel rather than the good men in his family.

Ahaz had many good role models, yet he chose to not follow after them. It's important for us to pay attention to who we are following in life. Who is your role model? Why do you follow them? Is this someone who does what is right in the eyes of the Lord?

S—The S stands for *Scripture*

O—The O stands for *Observation*

A—The A stands for *Application*

K—The K stands for *Kneeling in Prayer*

So they feared the Lord
but also served their own gods.

2 Kings 17:33

Reflection Question:

Israel fell to the Assyrians because they had sinned against the Lord and committed idolatry. They had stubborn hearts that refused to listen and turn from their evil ways and so the Lord afflicted them. The priests during this time were corrupt and worldly and so Israel feared the Lord but also served their own gods. Their children and their children's children did likewise.

The people of Israel loved the world and stubbornly clung to their idols, while also attempting to fear God. Their children followed in their footsteps. We are role models to our children and our children's children. Is there anything that you love that is worldly, that you need to let go of? Do you have an idol in your life or something that competes for your love over God? It's time to tear that idol down. Name it and pray and ask the Lord to give you the strength to overcome this worldly desire.

S—The S stands for *Scripture*

O—The O stands for *Observation*

A—The A stands for *Application*

K—The K stands for *Kneeling in Prayer*

He trusted in the Lord,

the God of Israel.

2 Kings 18:5

Reflection Question:

Hezekiah was a good and wise king who loved the Lord and protected his people. He removed the idols in Judah, including Moses' bronze serpent. He did not give way to fear when he was threatened or when his people were promised a peaceful and plentiful life by their enemies. Instead he was wise, and he advised his people to remain silent. He trusted in God.

Hezekiah destroyed Moses's bronze serpent. That serpent was a reminder of how God took care of his people in the wilderness, but even good things can become bad things, when we turn them into an idol. Yesterday, we wrote down some of the idols in our lives that come from the world's influence. Today I want you to consider, is there something good in your life that has become an idol? Have you found your identity in something other than God, for example being a wife, mom, your career, a talent or the work you do at church? These are all good things, but they must not compete with God and your worship of Him. Write a prayer below handing over anything good that competes with your affection for God, asking him to help you keep him first in your life.

S—The S stands for *Scripture*

O—The O stands for *Observation*

A—The A stands for *Application*

K—The K stands for *Kneeling in Prayer*

O Lord, the God of Israel,

enthroned above the cherubim,

you are the God, you alone,

of all the kingdoms of the earth;

you have made heaven and earth.

2 Kings 19:15

Reflection Question:

When Hezekiah received a letter from the king of Assyria, he immediately took that letter to the house of the Lord, spread it out before the Lord and prayed. While the king of Assyria was strong, Hezekiah knew that the God of Israel, who sits enthroned above the cherubim, who is the maker of the heavens and the earth—is stronger. And so, he prayed, and the Lord answered his prayers by sending an angel to strike down 185,000 Assyrians in the night!

Look at how Hezekiah addressed God in his prayer. When you pray, do you take the time to imagine God as he is, enthroned by cherubim, as the maker of heaven and earth? How does taking your eyes off of how big your problem is and focusing on how big your God is, change your prayers? If you have a concern today, take it to the throne of God now in prayer, addressing God as Hezekiah did.

S—The S stands for *Scripture*

O—The O stands for *Observation*

A—The A stands for *Application*

K—The K stands for *Kneeling in Prayer*

Thus says the Lord,

"I have heard your prayer:

I have seen your tears.

I will heal you."

2 Kings 20:5

Reflection Question:

When Hezekiah learned that he would die soon, he cried out to the Lord. God heard his prayer and gave him an extra 15 years of life. God even gave him a sign to reassure him. God blessed Hezekiah with wealth, victory, honor and a prolonged life but Hezekiah did not grow godlier in his old age. Instead, he became prideful and self-centered and did not end as well as he finished.

We have no control over how many days our life will be. But what we do know is that God is always near to us and he hears our prayers. Had Hezekiah not prayed, he would have died. Prayer matters. Also, ending well matters. Examine your life. Are there any areas where you used to be strong and have grown weaker? Is there anything you have not asked of God, that you should take to him in prayer?

S—The S stands for *Scripture*

O—The O stands for *Observation*

A—The A stands for *Application*

K—The K stands for *Kneeling in Prayer*

Behold, I am bringing upon
Jerusalem and Judah such disaster
that the ears of everyone
who hears of it will tingle.

2 Kings 21:12

Reflection Question:

When God said that King Manassah had done more evil than the Amorites, this was saying a lot! The Amorites were violent, immoral, godless people. And so severe judgement was pronounced by the prophets. He said the judgement would be so severe that the ears of everyone who heard about it, would tingle. The nation of Israel continually fell into sin as they followed one bad king after another. While I love focusing on the love, grace and mercy of our Heavenly Father, we must not forget that God hates and disciplines evil. What evil have you seen in your own nation? Let's pray for our nation and our nation's leaders today. Write your prayer below.

2 Kings 21

S—The S stands for *Scripture*

O—The O stands for *Observation*

A—The A stands for *Application*

K—The K stands for *Kneeling in Prayer*

Because your heart was penitent,

and you humbled yourself before the Lord

I have heard you, declares the Lord.

2 Kings 22:19

Reflection Question:

When the Book of the Law was found in the house of the Lord, Josiah was brokenhearted that the law was not being kept. He wanted to please God and God saw his heart and humility and heard his cries.

Man looks at the outer appearance, but God looks at the heart. (1 Samuel 16:7) Josiah's heart was soft towards God's word and will. God saw this and blessed him. How is your heart today? Are there any areas where it has grown cold, hard, numb or calloused? Identify those areas and ask the Lord to break your heart with the things that break his heart.

S—The S stands for *Scripture*

O—The O stands for *Observation*

A—The A stands for *Application*

K—The K stands for *Kneeling in Prayer*

Before him there was no king like him,

who turned to the Lord with all his heart

and with all his soul and with all his might

nor did any like him arise after him.

2 Kings 23:25

Reflection Question:

David, Solomon and Hezekiah were great kings, but Josiah was remarkable because of his godliness in the midst of a dark time. He stood out as a godly leader, who obeyed the Lord, during a time when evil was abounding everywhere in Israel.

Josiah followed the Lord with all of his heart, all of his soul and all of his might! Reflect on your own life. Are you following the Lord with ALL of your heart, ALL of your soul and ALL of your might? Sometimes we can get out of balance. What is one area where you need to grow?

2 Kings 23

S—The S stands for *Scripture*

O—The O stands for *Observation*

A—The A stands for *Application*

K—The K stands for *Kneeling in Prayer*

For because of the anger of the Lord

it came to the point in Jerusalem and Judah

that he cast them out from his presence.

2 Kings 24:20

Reflection Question:

God's prophetic word was fulfilled when Judah went into exile. God allowed King Nebuchadnezzar to steal the treasures of the house of the Lord and capture all the people of Jerusalem including the warriors, craftsmen, smiths, the king and his royal family.

God warned the kings of Israel over and over to turn from their wicked ways, but they refused to listen to the prophets of their day. As a result, they faced severe consequences for their waywardness. Because of Jesus' death on the cross covering our sins, we do not have to live in fear of God's judgement. But we still sin and because we sin, we face sorrow, broken relationships and other kinds of pain in our lives. Can you think of a time, when you were disciplined for something sinful in your life? What consequences did you face? Is there anything in your life that you need to repent of today? Confess it now and commit to changing your ways.

S—The S stands for *Scripture*

O—The O stands for *Observation*

A—The A stands for *Application*

K—The K stands for *Kneeling in Prayer*

So Jehoiachin put off his prison garments.

And every day of his life

he dined regularly at the king's table.

2 Kings 25:29

Reflection Question:

As we come to the end of 2 Kings, the story does not end here for Israel. The only surviving king of Israel, Jehoiachin, takes off his prison garments and dines at the kings table! He is restored and his needs are met the rest of his days. God's promises to David and his family line still stand, as we see a glimmer of hope in this final chapter of 2 Kings.

Our God is a God of restoration. There is always hope with Jesus! Who do you know that has fallen away from the Lord? Write a prayer below for their restoration. Keep believing and keep walking with the King.

2 Kings 25

S—The S stands for *Scripture*

O—The O stands for *Observation*

A—The A stands for *Application*

K—The K stands for *Kneeling in Prayer*